# SEA
# WINGS

Curtiss HS-2L flying boat of the Air
Board inspecting fishing boats on the
Fraser River, B.C., 1921.

# SEA WINGS

## A PICTORIAL HISTORY OF CANADA'S WATERBORNE DEFENCE AIRCRAFT

By J.A. Foster

**METHUEN**
Toronto New York London Sydney Auckland

Acknowledgement and thanks to the Atlantic Canada Aviation Museum Society, Shearwater Aviation Museum, Maritime Command Museum, Larry Milberry, National Aviation Museum, Public Archives Canada (PAC), and the research provided by Tony Melski, without whose help this book could never have been completed.

**Canadian Cataloguing in Publication Data**

Foster, Tony, 1932-
  Sea wings

ISBN 0-458-80410-x

1. Airplanes, Military. 2. Aircraft carriers. 3. Naval aviation. 4. Canada. Royal Canadian Navy - Aviation. I. Title.

VG95.C3F67 1986  623.74'6  C86-0924229-5

Front cover: A Fairey Firefly of the Royal Canadian Navy taking wave-off aboard HMCS *Warrior* near Halifax, N.S., May 1946. (George Gadde photo, DND, Public Archives of Canada PA131482)

Back cover: A Grumman Tracker over Mountain View in 1972. (Larry Milberry)

Design: Robin Brass
Printed and bound in Canada
1 2 3 4  86 90 89 88 87

# CONTENTS

A Supermarine Stranraer taking off.
The "Stran" was the RCAF's largest
aircraft in the days immediately
before the Second World War.

Shearwater Aviation Museum

A Fairey Firefly is prepared for launching from the
deck of HMCS *Warrior,* Kingston, Jamaica,
November 14, 1946.

G.E. Salter/DND/PAC PA141263

# FOREWORD

Canada's enduring romance with aviation has been the result of an exciting series of individual accomplishments and innovations, forward-thinking business decisions, heroic military actions and a degree of professionalism second to none. As a young and vigorous nation, we quickly saw the potential of aircraft to span our vast land and embraced the new profession of aviation with the enthusiasm of youth.

As our country developed and matured, so did our capabilities in aviation, allowing us to make a significant contribution to victory in two world wars. When peace returned in 1945, aviation became increasingly important in Canadian life with the emergence of a modern aircraft and avionics industry which, despite its ups and downs, has produced some of the finest specialized aircraft in the world.

With the frontier style of aviation so characteristic of the Canadian scene, which relies on the landing areas provided by mother nature, we have long had a special interest in the development of aircraft capable of operating from water. Even the early days of the RCAF were spent largely in civil duties carried out by float- and ski-equipped aircraft. In this fascinating collection of historical photographs, J.A. Foster skilfully leads us through that part of our military aviation heritage that is linked to water, both fresh and salt. While this is but a part of the whole, it nonetheless encompasses the entire timespan of Canadian aviation, from the daring exploits of Alexander Graham Bell's "chief test pilot," Casey Baldwin, to the present, when the formidable Aurora and capable veteran Sea King provide our only far-ranging maritime aviation capability.

Naval aviation deservedly occupies a considerable space in this book. It all came together—carrier, aircraft, air and ground crews, and shore base—on March 31, 1946, when HMCS *Warrior* arrived off Halifax and launched her aircraft to RCNAS Dartmouth. Inexperience and technical problems contributed to a shaky start, but over the next twenty-three years a highly professional force of carrier- and destroyer-based aircraft emerged that was as competent as any in the world. It is hardly surprising that the loss of such a hard-earned and valuable capability would cause much heartache.

The decision to pay off HMCS *Bonaventure* was the result of a budgetary squeeze that had started three years earlier, and the navy could no longer afford the manpower costs for the thousand-odd crew of the carrier. Some small consolation can be had by projecting the cost of the inevitable replacement of the carrier and her aircraft at some future date, a cost which only a few large nations can bear. Perhaps after all, it was only a matter of time.

ADMIRAL ROBERT H. FALLS, CMM, CD, CF (Ret.)

The *Silver Dart* flown by J.A.D. McCurdy makes the
first powered flight by a heavier-than-air machine in
Canada, Baddeck, N.S., February 23, 1909.

PAC PA61741

# THE BEGINNING

The first Canadian experiments with heavier-than-air machines on water were done in 1907 by Alexander Graham Bell and his young engineering associates, John A.D. McCurdy and F.W. "Casey" Baldwin. Bell maintained a summer home and laboratory at Beinn Bhreagh, across the water from Baddeck, Nova Scotia. Among his dozens of interests was a fascination for tetrahedral kite construction and the possibility of applying its principles to aircraft construction.

Four years had passed since the Wrights had flown their fragile machine at Kitty Hawk, North Carolina. Powered flight still remained little more than an expensive novelty for a self-indulgent few willing to risk their lives. The forces which held kites and aircraft aloft, it was believed, came from the action of air beneath the wings and fuselage. Bell assumed—incorrectly—that an aircraft design based on the tetrahedral V-shape would prove to be the most efficient type of flying machine.

Testing his theory meant building and then towing model kites at various speeds and directions under different wind conditions, much the way the Wrights had tested their glider at Kill Devil Hill, N.C., in 1900. But the only area with a flat cleared surface close to Baddeck was the great inland waters of the Bras d'Or Lakes. To fly his kites Bell needed to design and build pontoons. Throughout the summer of 1906, to the amusement of the locals, the two young men and their 60-year-old patron worked on the development of Bell's theories.

In stiff summer breezes model kites were towed by motorboats while the men measured wind velocities, altitudes and lift. If the weather turned sour they worked indoors, designing and testing ideas for aircraft controls, engines and propellers.

During a visit to his home in Washington, Bell interviewed young Lieutenant Thomas E. Selfridge, a recent West Point graduate, who stoutly believed, despite scepticism from his superiors, that flying machines would one day become an important branch of the military. Impressed by the lad's enthusiam, Bell arranged a leave of absence through President Roosevelt so Selfridge could join the team in Baddeck as an observer.

To power his giant tetrahedral kite *Cygnet* Bell needed a motor. He approached Glenn H. Curtiss, a motorcycle racer and manufacturer in Hammondsport, New York, to build a lightweight engine. The stone-faced 39-year-old Curtiss was only interested in three things: machinery, speed and money. He had won the world's record for the fastest mile by any machine, on a motorcycle of his own design. As a businessman he was quick to grasp the potential for profit in Bell's aviation experiments. He arrived at Baddeck by steamer in September to install his new motor.

Mabel Bell watched the enthusiasm of her husband and his four associates working on the tetrahedral project and conceived the idea of the Aerial Experiment Association. It came into being on October 12, 1907. Financed with

$20,000 from Mrs. Bell, the AEA was given a one-year mandate to put a man into the air. Initially the associates would work to complete the float-equipped tetrahedral kite, after which each man would have the assistance of the others on a flying machine of his own design.

By early December the *Cygnet* was ready for a manned flight test. It resembled a huge wedge of honeycomb with its hundreds of tetrahedral shaped cells that the Baddeck women had spent months covering with red silk. Selfridge was given the honour of piloting its first flight. Baldwin and McCurdy helped him crawl into the tiny tunnel cockpit, where he lay face down, able to see only directly in front of him. A tow line connected the kite to the local passenger steamer, *Blue Hill*, which had been hired for the occasion. A man with an axe was delegated to cut the tow rope. Bell followed in a motorboat in case of an accident.

At full speed the steamer turned into the wind. The huge kite lifted quickly to well over a 150 feet, where it "flew with great steadiness for several minutes . . . seemingly glued to one spot in the sky." Finally, during a lull in the wind it descended, alighting so gently that Selfridge was unaware he was no longer airborne. In the excitement of success the tow line was forgotten and the steamer dragged the kite violently through the water, completely destroying it.

Selfridge managed to swim clear. Bell's hopes for mounting the Curtiss engine in a manned and float-equipped tetrehedral aircraft were dashed.

At Curtiss' suggestion, AEA operations were moved to Hammondsport for the balance of the winter. After a series of gliding experiments a motor was installed in an aircraft designed by Selfridge, nicknamed *Red Wing* because of its red silk wing covering. On March 12, 1908, from the frozen surface of Lake Keuka near Hammondsport, Casey Baldwin flew the machine through the air

Alexander Graham Bell's tetrahedral kite *Cygnet* on pontoons and (facing page) flying near Baddeck, N.S., on August 9, 1906. Bell is seated in the stern of the tow boat.

under power a distance of 319 feet. It was the first powered flight by a Canadian, the first aircraft to operate on skis and the first public demonstration of a flying machine in North America (the Wright brothers' flights had been made privately).

Five days later while *Red Wing* was airborne a wind gust caught it, and Baldwin lost control and crashed. The accident proved that simply shifting the pilot's weight was not enough to control an aircraft. Accordingly Baldwin's design of *White Wing*, the AEA's second experimental aircraft, incorporated hinged tips into the wings connected to the pilot's seat by wires. Now when the plane tilted it could be returned to horizontal flight.

In September at the Coney Island race track when McCurdy explained to French airman, Henri Farman, how the new wing flaps operated, Farman's eyes lit up. "Ah," he exclaimed. "Ailerons!" His name for the "little wings" stuck.

The next machine, *June Bug*, designed by Curtiss, gave a very poor performance on its first flight. Suspecting that air might be leaking through the porous cotton wing covers, Baldwin and McCurdy suggested smearing the fabric with linseed oil—the first recorded instance of aircraft fabric being "doped." On July

The *Query*, Bell's experimental hydrofoil at Baddeck, September 21, 1909. Later versions reached speeds of 70 mph. The RN and USN, though interested in using the design for World War I sub-chasers, refused to allow Bell production control over the new craft.

4, 1908, at Hammondsport and piloted by Curtiss, the *June Bug* completed the world's first successful measured kilometre by a heavier-than-air machine to win the *Scientific American* Trophy. The event was described by Bell's daughter, Daisy Fairchild:

"The first flight raised excitement to the boiling point, and as Mr. Curtiss flew over the red flag that marked the finish and away on toward the trees, I don't think any of us quite knew what we were doing. One lady was so absorbed as not to hear the coming train and was struck by the engine and had two ribs broken."

Selfridge was ordered back to Washington in August and appointed to the newly formed Aeronautical Board of the U.S. Army. The following month, during a test flight with Orville Wright at Fort Myer, Virginia, he was killed when the Wright-designed aircraft in which they were flying crashed. Although seriously injured, Orville survived. Selfridge's loss was a bitter personal blow to Bell and the other AEA associates.

Bell brought *June Bug* to Baddeck. After renaming it *Loon* he converted it to a "hydroplane," equipping it with a set of pontoons that he had designed. Unfortunately the flight tests conducted during November were unsatisfactory. The air-cooled Curtiss engine simply wasn't powerful enough to lift the aircraft, pilot and floats off the water.

*Silver Dart*, the last of the AEA designs, was equipped with a more powerful water-cooled Curtiss motor. Bell arranged to bring it to Baddeck for flight testing. There, on February 23, 1909, McCurdy took off from the frozen surface of Bras d'Or Lake and flew *Silver Dart* a distance of half a mile while the delighted townspeople looked on. It was the first flight by a British subject in a powered heavier-than-air machine in the British Empire. Mabel Bell described the event in a letter to her daughter, Daisy:

"Another perfect day, the *Silver Dart* made a short flight, coming down because the land was near. . . . We all pleaded with Papa for another flight but he was firm. It was the first flight of an airship in Canada and he would take no chances of disaster to spoil this first success."

Next day McCurdy piloted *Silver Dart* on a circuitous flight lasting six minutes. The AEA disbanded in March 1909. No other pioneer aviation group ever contributed as many innovative ideas. The lessons learned by Bell and his associates formed the basis for all subsequent successful aircraft development. Curtiss returned to Hammondsport to begin commercial exploitation of the AEA ideas— ailerons, pontoons, the tricycle steerable undercarriage, airfoils, rudder and control surfaces—which, together with his engine designs, became the basis for the Curtiss Aircraft Company and, later, the Curtiss-Wright Corporation.

With financial backing from Bell, J.A.D. McCurdy and Casey Baldwin formed the Canadian Aerodrome Company for the purpose of manufacturing flying machines at Beinn Bhreagh. *Baddeck No.1* and *No.2* were the first two aircraft built. With these machines and the *Silver Dart* the partners hoped to demonstrate the importance of flying machines to the Canadian government. They secured an invitation to perform "a demonstration on the art of flying" at Camp Petawawa, near Ottawa. *Silver Dart* and *Baddeck No.1* were crated and shipped there by train.

On August 2, 1909, before a sceptical audience of military officers and government officials, *Silver Dart* made five separate flights of 50 mph at an altitude of 50 feet. On the fifth go-around, McCurdy, blinded by the sun and unfamiliar with the soft sandy soil of the cavalry grounds, clipped a knoll and crashed. Fortunately he walked away from the accident but the *Silver Dart* was a write-off.

A week later *Baddeck No.1* was ready for demonstration. Once more officialdom assembled. On the first attempt the engine developed ignition trouble. The spectators dispersed to the Officers Mess. Next day, only 70 yards after take-off, the tail-heavy machine slid ungracefully backwards to earth. Again McCurdy walked away. The bureaucrats enjoyed a good chuckle at the farcical proceedings and returned to Ottawa in good humour. Their consensus was that flying machines were little more than amusing toys with no practical military value. If they were to be developed further it was a matter for the private

PAC C17357

PAC C76017

(Left) The members of the Aerial Experiment Association, which came into being in 1907 at the suggestion of Mrs. Bell. Left to right, Glenn Curtiss, J.A.D.McCurdy, Alexander Graham Bell, Casey Baldwin and Lieut. Thomas Selfridge.

The *June Bug* (below) was renamed *Loon* and mounted on floats but proved too underpowered to take off from the water. Note the wing-tip aileron controls.

sector. This attitude remained fixed in military minds throughout North America and Europe until the outbreak of war. Discouraged but not defeated, McCurdy and Baldwin returned to their drawing boards at Beinn Bhreagh.

Credit for the first aeroplane to take off and land on water under its own power goes to Henri Fabre, son of a Marseilles ship owner. On March 28, 1910, Fabre's strange-looking *Hydravion* lifted from the harbor of Le Mede near Marseilles, flew 500 metres, then settled gracefully back on to the calm water. It was his first flight in a heavier-than-air machine.

In building the *Hydravion* Fabre used a canard-form design with tail surfaces forward, wings, motor and a pusher propeller aft. Two wooden girders formed the fuselage. He sat astride the top one on a small seat with his feet resting on a pair of rudder pedals that allowed him to warp the wings for lateral control. A stick controlled the aircraft's elevators and rudder. The fabric flying surfaces covered only the top of the wing and were affixed to the end of each rib with spring hooks allowing

them to be tightened, detached or reefed, like a sail. Power was provided by one of the newly-developed light 50 hp Gnome rotary engines.

The *Hydravion* sat on three small flat floats that looked very much like stubby airfoil wing sections. At rest the floats were practically submerged, but once under way they lifted from the water and skipped across the surface until flying speed was obtained. The following year Fabre built a set of floats for a land-based Voisin biplane, thereby collecting credit for creating the world's first amphibious aircraft. Sadly, as with most aviation innovators of the times, Fabre ran out of funds needed to continue his experiments.

Two months after Fabre's historic flight, Glenn Curtiss flew a landplane non-stop from Albany to New York. In case of a force landing on the Hudson River he had fitted the aircraft with a nose hydro-ski, wing-tip floats and a canvas tube filled with cork. Curtiss had already patented most of the AEA designs for his own company. Spurred by the market potential for float-equipped and amphibious aircraft for the U.S. Navy, he concentrated on developing an acceptable prototype machine.

The *Loon* at speed, Baddeck, November 1908.

On the morning of November 14, 1910, a Curtiss wheeled pusher biplane became the first aircraft to take off from a ship when Eugene Ely lifted from the deck of the USS *Birmingham* anchored in Hampton Roads, Virginia. Three months later Ely capped this feat by landing on the deck of the USS *Pennsylvania* in San Francisco Bay.

Farther down the Pacific coast at San Diego on January 26, 1911, Curtiss finally made his first water take-off, using a pusher biplane equipped with a single central float and stabilizing outriggers. In the next few months he flew the first aircraft using parallel floats, demonstrating their natural lateral stability, carried the first pasenger off the water and flew the first successful boat-hulled aircraft. He developed an amphibious aircraft, then arranged to have one of his seaplanes lowered onto the water from a warship, flown, and winched back aboard.

To Curtiss belongs the concept of the "stepped hull" that breaks the suction between floats and water during take-off, a principle now used by every speedboat and pontoon manufacturer in the world. In 1912 he manufactured a two-seat "Aeroyacht" biplane for the very wealthy. Henry Ford, the great automotive innovator, visited the Curtiss factory for a personal demonstration. But the real commercial breakthrough came with an order from the U.S. Navy for 150 boat-hulled Curtiss Model F aircraft. This machine was the first to fly with Elmer A. Sperry's new gyroscopic autopilot.

With its huge land mass, myriads of lakes and rivers providing natural runways, and an enormous undeveloped and still largely unexplored hinterland, Canada was ripe for float-equipped aircraft. The first "hydroplane" flight in Canada was made from Toronto Harbour on July 6, 1912, by Fred G. Eels in a Rieflin biplane. On July 17, at Port Stanley, Ontario, Walter Brookins took off and landed in a Burgess-Wright biplane, and in the next few days two passengers flew with him—Dora Labatt and Lorne Bradley, the first Canadians to fly as passengers in a seaplane.

A year later in Vancouver, British Columbia, Alys McKay Bryant soloed in a Curtiss biplane to become the first woman to pilot an aircraft in Canada; her husband, Johnny Bryant, became the country's first aviation fatality when he crashed in the same aircraft. Aviation in Canada had come of age.

PAC C20260

PAC C10999

(Top) *Baddeck No 1* at Petawawa for demonstrations to the military, August 1909, and (below) the "air ship bunch," left to right: unknown, Professor Charles Manley, John A.D. McCurdy, unknown, F.W. "Casey" Baldwin, unknown.

(Facing page) Two milestones: Glenn Curtiss in his "hydroplane" after making the first successful take-off from water, San Diego, January 26, 1911, and (below) the Benoist flying boat at the St. Petersburg-Tampa Airboat Lines inaugural, January 1, 1914.

Squadron Commander E.H. Dunning, in a Sopwith Pup, makes the first-ever landing of an aircraft on a warship at sea, HMS *Furious*, August 2, 1917. The ship sailed full-steam-ahead into the wind, so that the air flow over the deck was roughly the landing speed of the Pup. Thus the Pup virtually hovered over the deck so that the pilot's fellow officers could grab it when he cut the throttle. Dunning died attempting to repeat the experiment.

# WORLD WAR I

"Nothing so spurs man's inventiveness as the thought of losing a war. . . ." Although Winston Churchill was referring to the first appearance of British tanks clanking across no-man's land during the 1916 Battle of the Somme, he could just as easily have been speaking about the airplane. The "amusing toy" had suddenly become a weapon of war. Maritime aircraft were used by both sides in the conflict, first in reconnaissance roles, later as bombers and finally as torpedo carriers.

Seaplane carriers were developed: HMS *Ark Royal,* a 7500-ton converted collier, became England's first—and the first of several to bear that name. Several cross-Channel steamers were converted. With cranes installed, each ship could carry three or four seaplanes. The famous German raider *Wolf,* operating in the Indian and Pacific oceans, carried a Friedrichshafen seaplane on board to locate most of the 28 Allied vessels it sank.

In 1915, applications were being accepted from the Colonies and Dominions by the newly incorporated Royal Naval Air Service. Any Canadian wishing to be considered was first required to obtain a pilot's licence at his own expense. To train pilots the Curtiss Aviation School was organized near Toronto at Long Branch, using Curtiss JN-3s on wheels and Curtiss F flying boats. The school's flying boats were based at Hanlan's Point in Toronto Harbour. On July 11, Homer Smith and Strachan Ince became the first two pupils to graduate as pilots from a Canadian

flying school. That same summer in Toronto, Curtiss Aeroplanes & Motors Limited under the management of J.A.D. McCurdy became the first aircraft manufacturing plant in Canada.

Early the following year the first RNAS unit was formed and ready for action. The new Naval Wing was equipped with Sopwith Strutters, two-seater biplanes used previously for bombing. Forty Canadians were in the group. Before the war ended 12 became leading naval fighter "aces"—although not while flying Strutters. This unstable machine had an alarming inclination to shed its wings or spin out in a steep turn when trying to avoid enemy aircraft. "Observe, bomb then run like hell" was one pilot's succinct description of his flying time in Strutters.

Fortunately by late 1916 the naval squadrons were given speedier and more manoeuvrable French Nieuports and Sopwith Pups with which to fight. Their task was to defend naval bases along the French and Belgian coast. By the end of the war the Royal Navy used huge Felixstowe F.2A flying boats as patrol aircraft. These carried a four-man crew and up to seven machine guns.

As the war dragged on and British losses mounted, a critical shortage of aircrews developed. The War Office accepted an offer from a group of Canadian industrialists who, together with the Imperial Munitions Board, built a factory and flying school in Toronto. The Royal Flying Corps overseas Canadian military pilot

M.C. Dubuc Collection/PAC PA135600

Nieuport of the RNAS preparing for training
flight, 1916.

training program began. This action effectively
ended most civil aviation activities in the country until after the war. The 6$\frac{1}{2}$ -acre factory of
Canadian Aeroplanes Ltd. was built in less
than three months. In addition to producing
Curtiss JN-4 Canuck training aircraft, the
company produced 30 large Felixstowe F.5L
flying boats for the U.S. Navy. By 1918 its
flight school was sending 200 pilots per
month across to England. When the war ended, Canada, with less than two per cent of the
Empire's population, had produced fully a
third of the pilots for the RFC (which became
the Royal Air Force after April 18, 1918).

Although the Canadians were never
faulted for bravery or enthusiasm, their military
conduct remained open to question by a few

of the tight-lipped British commanding officers.
Lieutenant Hambley was a case in point. The
CO of his training squadron in England wrote
of him: "In my opinion this officer is completely
untrustworthy and casual. During the period
he was with the squadron he was a continual
source of trouble and personally I should
hesitate to believe anything he said."

Yet there was another side to the Canadian; a British pilot who flew combat with him
wrote: "Old Hambley is a very bad Canadian
and if I wasn't out here I should have difficulty
in seeing any good in him at all. . . . He used
to . . . say things that no subaltern should say
to a CO. He was uncouth and used to bring
terrible Canadians into the Mess and the
major wanted me to get rid of him but I said I

20

would rather not. He drinks too much, wears sidewhiskers and sometimes a dirty stock. But he is a splendid fellow and I have the utmost confidence in him over the line."

With America's entry in the war, the U.S. Navy supplied Curtiss HS-2L flying boats. Based at Dartmouth, North Sydney and Baker Point, they flew on submarine patrols along Canada's East Coast to counteract the growing German U-boat menace in the North Atlantic. Taking a page from the U.S. and British navies, on September 5, 1918, Canada created the Royal Canadian Naval Air Service to operate these aircraft, only to disband it three months later, before the personnel had finished training, as a frivolous and unnecessary peacetime luxury.

When the war ended Canadian pilots had produced the lion's share of enemy aircraft shot down: Billy Bishop led with 72 kills. Naval pilot Ray Collishaw was third with 60, followed by D.R. MacLaren with 54 and W.G. Barker with 53. Four Canadian naval pilots scored more than 20. Without their high-scoring Canadians the flying achievements of the RAF and RNAS would have been considerably more modest, a fact not lost on the British government even before the cessation of hostilities. In June 1918 the Secretary of State commented about the "very high standards of the semi-trained Canadians."

Had the Secretary of State taken the trouble to investigate the performance discrepancy between British and the "semi-trained" Canadian pilots, he would have discovered that while Canada spent $10,000 per man just on his preliminary training, the British spent only half that amount per man for an entire pilot training program. In addition to superior training the wild Canadians in the RAF and RNAS for some reason were endowed with the best temperament for fighter pilots.

A month before the outbreak of war, Sir Douglas Haig, the British Army Commander-in-Chief, had told a military gathering at Aldershot: "I hope none of you gentlemen is so foolish as to think that aeroplanes will be able to be usefully employed for reconnaissance in the air. There is only one way for a commander to get information by reconnaissance and that is by the use of cavalry." At war's end he saw no reason to change this opinion. In his final dispatch a mere two sentences were given grudgingly to the air: "Though aircraft and tanks proved of enormous value, their true value is as ancillaries of infantry, artillery and cavalry. . . . The killing power of the aeroplane is still very limited as compared to the three principal arms."

Sopwith Strutter $1^1/_2$. The first British tractor two-seater with the observer in the rear, it entered service in July 1916 during the Battle of the Somme and served briefly with the Royal Naval Air Service as a strategic daylight bomber.

(Above) A Sopwith on floats at Hamble Bay.        (Below) A Fairey Campania, used as a shipboard seaplane.

(Above) A Nieuport Baby two-seater.

(Below) A line-up of Canadian-made Curtiss JN-4s of the RFC Canada at Camp Leaside, 1917.

Elmer Fullerton (right) and unidentified
person with an Avro 504, c.1918.
Fullerton served with the Royal Canadian
Engineers in Europe from 1916 to 1917.
He transferred to the Royal Naval Air
Service, then to the Royal Air Force.
He joined the Canadian Air Force in
1920, becoming flying instructor at
Camp Borden. He was the pilot of one
of the two Junkers aircraft on the famous
exploration flight down the Mackenzie
Valley in 1921, in which both propellers
were broken and new ones were fashioned
by hand. His posts during World War II
included CO of the Service Flying
Training School at Summerside, P.E.I.,
and base commander at Trenton. He was
awarded the McKee Trophy in 1934.

A Felixstowe F.5 flying boat built by
Canadian Aeroplanes Ltd. at Toronto,
July 1918.

E.G. Fullerton Collection/PAC C57702

PAC PA24461

PAC C18860

A Sopwith Pup of the RNAS takes off from the gun turret platform of HMAS *Sydney*, c.1918. A number of warships were fitted with such platforms. As the gun turret could be swivelled, the ship did not have to head into the wind to launch the plane.

PAC PA122515

Billy Bishop in a Nieuport, 1917. Canada's leading World War I fighter ace went on to become an air vice marshal.

25

(Above) S/L Raymond Collishaw and pilots with Sopwith F.1 Camels of No.203 Squadron, RAF, at Allonville, France, July 1918. Collishaw was formerly commander of No.10 Squadron, RNAS.

Canadians joining the RNAS trained in the Curtiss JN-3 "Jenny." The Curtiss School of Aviation was set up in 1915 at Long Branch, Ont. Canada's first air ace trained there was F/L Edward R. Grange, who served with 1 (Naval) Squadron. Later model JN-4 trainers of the RFC in Canada were built by Canadian Aeroplanes Ltd.

(Above) Flight cadets of the newly formed Canadian Naval Air Service, Ottawa, 1918. German U-boat activity in 1917 prompted the British Admiralty to ask Canada for anti-sub patrols. The RCNAS was the result.

(Below) Launching US Navy Curtiss HS-2L at Dartmouth, June 1919. The HS-2L was used for Atlantic U-boat patrol during World War I. After the war two were used by the St. Maurice Fire Protection Association for patrolling the St. Maurice River Valley of Quebec. Indians on the Senneterre Reserve called the aircraft *Kitchi Chghee*, meaning "Big Duck."

Refuelling the Empire flying boat *Cabot* from the
Harrow tanker, July 30, 1939. As war clouds gathered,
the British Air Ministry became vitally interested in
learning how practical in-flight refuelling would be
for coastal patrol aircraft. A series of tests was
undertaken over Southampton Water with satisfactory
results. This in-flight refuelling method was then used
by Imperial Airways for its transatlantic service between
August and October 1939.

John Stroud Collection

# THE YEARS OF COMPLACENCY

Thousands of pilots and mechanics came home from the war anxious to use their newly acquired aviation talents. They purchased war-surplus aircraft and went out to look for work. But the only civil flying available was giving rides. Pretty tame stuff after the excitement of combat. Men and aircraft crisscrossed the country visiting every likely looking town or village, searching for passengers. Any level field served as an airstrip. People came from miles around to gawk. A few, with change in their pockets, went for a ride. "Barnstorming" entered the English vocabulary. If business was slow, a pilot might put on a low-level aerobatic show to stir a little excitement. As the stunts became more spectacular there were accidents. Regulations were needed to enforce the public safety. A federal Air Board came into being in 1919 to control all military and civil aviation in Canada.

It was to be a year of aviation firsts in Canada: the first offical airmail flew between Canada and the U.S. when Eddie Hubbard with William Boeing piloted a Boeing C3 seaplane between Vancouver and Seattle on March 3. Four months later John Alcock and Arthur Brown made the first direct transatlantic flight in a Vickers Vimy biplane from St. John's, Newfoundland, to Clifden, Ireland. The fact that the aircraft ended up on its nose in a bog was irrelevant. In July Frank Ellis made the first parachute jump by a Canadian in Canada from a Curtiss JN-4 biplane at Crystal Beach, Ontario.

Over on the West Coast Capt. Ernest Hoy flew the first aircraft across the Rockies from Vancouver to Calgary via Lethbridge, and in the east at Parrsboro, Nova Scotia, Majors Brackley and Gwan made the nation's first multi-passenger flight in a Handley Page bomber with 14 people on board.

Wartime aerial photographic reconnaissance had proved invaluable for analyzing enemy positions and intentions. Photographic mosaics of the entire Western Front were updated daily. In 1919 the same principles were applied to commercial peacetime use in Canada's first aerial survey. The H.V. Greene Aerial Survey Company Limited was formed to carry out a Labrador expedition. Two former U.S. Navy pilots took some 15,000 photographs of timberland.

The Laurentide Company, a Quebec pulp and paper manufacturer, arranged to borrow two Curtiss HS-2L flying boats from the Air Board to carry out a survey in the St. Maurice River valley. The timber owners and operators in the area formed the St. Maurice Forestry Protective Association. Stuart Graham, a former RNAS pilot, flew the machines from Dartmouth, N.S., to the base of operations at Lac à la Tortue. In addition to aerial photography and sketching timber limits, the aircraft were used for personnel transport and forest fire patrols. The directors of Laurentide soon decided they would prefer to purchase flying time rather than operate their own aircraft, and in 1922 Laurentide Air Service

Ltd. was formed to provide that service.

Private Pilot's licence No. 1 was issued January 24, 1920, to Stanley Scott of Ottawa. Three months later in Regina, Robert McCombie received Air Engineer certificate No. 1. On the same day in Regina, a Curtiss JN-4 biplane owned by the Aerial Service Company Ltd. donned the lettering G-CAAA to become the country's first commercially registered aircraft.

Hard on the heels of these bureaucratic developments came provisional approval on June 30, 1920, for establishing a Canadian Air Force composed of 1340 officers and 3905 enlisted men. Equipped with an assortment of Felixstowe F.3, Curtiss H-16 and ex-Naval Air Service HS-2L flying boats, the new air force spent the bulk of its flying time in a variety civil activities for various provinicial governments.

Aviation's post-war boom peaked in 1920. Then the novelty of heroic pilots and their aircraft began to wear thin. Those about the country who had wanted to experience the thrill of flying had already taken their trips with the barnstormers. Those that remained either weren't interested or didn't have any money. The unpleasant fact remained that except in specialized situations, flying could not be commercially justified. The nation slid into one of its periodic financial recessions. As the barnstorming business dried up and aircraft motors wore out, most of the pilots, older and wiser now, drifted into less hazardous occupations, married and settled down. For several years, with the exception of Laurentide Air Services, Canadian commercial aviation wallowed quietly in the doldrums.

In 1924 things began picking up. Incorporated officially on April Fools Day, the Royal Canadian Air Force emerged as the junior service of the armed forces. To equip it eight Vickers Viking IVs were ordered. Along the West Coast, these RCAF flying boats were used to patrol for illegal commercial fishing and apprehend rum runners racing high-powered speedboats across the Strait of Juan de Fuca to the thirsty American markets around Puget Sound. From Victoria Beach Station, Manitoba, an RCAF Vickers Viking completed an aerial survey of the Churchill River districts and Reindeer Lake. A 15,000-square-mile area was covered in less than a month. Until the threat of war in Europe during the late thirties, the RCAF remained a mainly civil flying operation, with such tasks as forestry patrols, photographic surveys and law enforcement. Most of its bases were the seaplane bases it inherited from the Air Board.

The Province of Ontario created its own private air force in 1924 with 13 Curtiss HS-2L flying boats, 16 pilots and 19 maintenance engineers. Based at Sault Ste. Marie, the aircraft were used for fire patrol, personnel transportation, ambulance work and surveys. One pilot, on forest fire patrol on July 5, flew an incredible10 hours 40 minutes. By the end of its first year men and machines had spotted 597 fires, covered 170,000 air miles and logged 2,595 hours in the air!

Technical innovations benefited fliers both civil and military. A man named Jack Elliot devised an all-weather canvas-covered nose hangar for servicing aircraft engines outdoors and was immediately canonized by every pilot, mechanic, apprentice and dock walloper who had ever frozen his fingers or fought off black flies while working in the bush on an aircraft. And in 1927 at Camp Borden a successful air test of the first controllable-pitch propeller took place. Its inventor, W.R. Turnbull, a middle-aged engineer from Rothesay, New Brunswick, had developed the idea in his homebuilt wind tunnel. With this discovery it finally became possible for a pilot to use take-off power and climb to cruising altitude with his propeller in flat pitch, then reduce his engine power and, from the cockpit, change his propeller's angle of attack to a coarser pitch for cruising. The controllable-pitch propeller improved the use of available engine power, producing a shorter take-off

Ernest W. Stedman Collection/PAC PA121930

Captain John Alcock and Lieutenant Arthur Brown made the first non-stop transatlantic flight in June 1919, taking off from Lester's Field, St. John's, Newfoundland, and landing in a bog in Ireland. Shown here are various scenes at their point of departure. In the photo at left, Alcock himself is seen loading supplies into the Vickers Vimy. They were in the air for 16 hours 27 minutes. It was five years before another aircraft crossed the North Atlantic

Reuben T. Parsons Collection/PAC PA121328

Ernest W. Stedman Collection/PAC PA121928

The Boeing C3 aircraft which inaugurated the first airmail service between Seattle, Wash., and Victoria, B.C., in 1920. Left to right, Eddie Hubbard, H.L. Bishop, Mr. Gardiner.

run on land or water and faster control response. It delivered a significant increase in aircraft range, since less fuel was required to cover the same distance as with a fixed-pitch propeller. Best of all there was less wear and tear on the engines. Most operating time in the air could now be spent loafing along at low rpm with propellers in coarse pitch.

Flying began to take on a practical nature. There had been breakthroughs in engine and aircraft designs. Design development for a new radial air-cooled engine had been sponsored by the U.S. Navy on the theory that a lighter, more reliable motor would translate into smaller and more efficient aircraft being carried on board naval vessels. Pratt & Whitney with their Wasp engine won the

contract in 1926. Radial air-cooled engines remained the power source on most aircraft until the introduction of turboprop and jet engines. With only minor improvements the Pratt & Whitney piston motors remained in production until the early fifties. High-wing cabin monoplanes with fixed undercarriages powered by the new engines slowly began replacing the slow lumbering biplanes with their in-line engines. High-wing monoplane design became the industry standard until 1932, when low-wing aircraft with retractable undercarriages were introduced.

The courageous starry-eyed amateurs who had done so much during the early years of development had left the scene. The era of "firsts" by aviation pioneers was drawing to a close. One notable achievement was a trans-Canada seaplane flight during September 1926 by Canadian Squadron Leader Earl Godfrey and J. Dalzell McKee, a wealthy American. It was the first time any airplane had covered the distance from Montreal to Vancouver. In gratitude for the assistance given by the various air stations and bases en route, McKee established a silver trophy to commemorate the event. The trophy was to be awarded annually to whoever was judged to have contributed the most to Canadian aviation. The "Trans Canada Trophy" became generally known as the "McKee Trophy." Harold A. "Doc" Oaks, a bush pilot, was its first winner, in 1927 ". . . in recognition of his work in organizing air services to outlying districts." Significantly, the first three winners were bush pilots, proof of the importance of these northern fliers to Canadian aviation.

In 1930 the Canadian government chartered a Fokker seaplane from Western Canada Airways for a scientific expedition into the Arctic. Flown by Walter Gilbert, the aircraft was sent out to plot lines of magnetic variation and angles of compass declination, circumnavigate King William Island and investigate the remains of the Sir John Franklin expedition of 1845-48. The project was a great success and did much to develop geographical knowledge of the Canadian Arctic. Gilbert became the 1933 McKee Trophy winner.

Until the Royal Canadian Mounted Police formed its own aviation branch in 1937, the Mounties depended on bush pilots and the RCAF to cover the sparsely inhabited north. Flying with RCMP officers, the pilots checked for illegal hunting, fishing and fur trapping, and periodically took part in criminal investigations. Murderer Albert Johnson, the celebrated "Mad Trapper of Rat River," was tracked by a posse of RCMP officers and deputies near Aklavik for several weeks without success. After a month of fruitless pursuit and running short of supplies, they called in a bush aircraft. Although Johnson hid whenever the plane flew over, "Wop" May was able to follow his tracks in the snow and lead the posse to its quarry, who was shot and killed.

Fairey IIIC seaplane of the Air Board. This was one of several planes used on legs of the first trans-Canada flight, from Halifax to Vancouver, October 7-17, 1920.

In 1935 Noorduyn Aircraft of Montreal developed Canada's first bush aircraft, the Norseman. Capable of operating on floats, skis or wheels and carrying up to 10 people, the rugged, single-engine Norseman became the choice of pilots and bush operators across the country because of its dependable service and ease of maintenance. By the time production ceased after World War II, Norseman aircraft were serving with the RCAF, the RCMP, provincial and state governments and the U.S. Army Air Corps, in addition to commercial operators around the world.

During the late twenties, the RCAF had begun a recruiting drive through Canadian universities to attract well educated officers and aircrew. A three-year well-paid pilot training course to wings standard was offered to undergraduates during the summer months at Camp Borden. Unfortunately, after the elections of 1930 the idea was abandoned as too expensive. The nation was in the midst of a depression, jobs were scarce, food and unemployment lines long, and the government short of cash for defence spending.

Camp Borden remained the primary training camp for the air force but its activities were severely curtailed. Optimists, however, were already planning a modern operational headquarters and training establishment at Trenton, Ontario, incorporating both land- and water-based aircraft when money became available. Meantime the defence establishment of all three armed services hunkered down to wait out the period of fiscal restraint. In a letter to Ottawa the commanding officer of the Camp Borden flying training school complained: "I seem to spend most of my time filling in requisition forms or answering silly questions in an attempt to justify the cost of gasoline and oil needed to fly the aircraft. How are our pilots expected to train in airplanes with empty fuel tanks?"

The Defence Department's succinct reply advised him to do the best with what he had. Not much help. Yet, despite the budget restrictions, by 1933 things were beginning to happen. No. 4 Squadron was reformed in Vancouver with flying boats. A year later a similar squadron, No. 5, established itself on the East Coast at Dartmouth, N.S., using float-equipped Fairchild 71 aircraft on RCMP rum-running patrols. The base, known as RCAF Eastern Passage Base, consisted of a single hangar with a sloping seaplane ramp and a dock, along with 70 men of all ranks. Their job, ridiculously, was to cover the eastern Canadian coastline from the Bay of Fundy to the Arctic Sea. As political tensions grew in Europe and the threat of war loomed, government purse strings gradually loosened.

In 1936 No. 6 Squadron, based at Trenton, was formed as a torpedo bomber unit flying the reliable old Vickers Vedettes. The following year the government wisely released the air force from its multi-purpose role and created the Department of Transport, forerunner of today's Ministry of Transport, to oversee matters of civil aviation, leaving military aviation strictly to the RCAF. The RCMP formed its own aviation section, releasing No. 5 Squadron from police patrols and turning it into strictly a coastal reconnaissance arm.

Canadian aircraft manufacturing received

a boost with an order for 18 Supermarine Stranraer flying boats to be built at Cartierville, Quebec, to replace the older Vickers Vedettes. Carrying a crew of nine plus practice bombs or depth charges, and with Lewis guns in the fore and aft turrets, the "Stran" could remain aloft for nine hours at a stretch, cruising at a sedate 110 mph. At the time it was the most advanced heavy aircraft in the Canadian arsenal. Today's private pilots would have found its radio and instrumentation primitive. Although the HF vacuum tube radio on board was capable of transmitting morse signals over considerable distances, voice communications between aircraft and the control tower were rarely possible even when flying in formation or in the traffic pattern directly over the tower!

By the outbreak of World War II the RCAF by contemporary standards was still minuscule. Staffed by 4061 officers and men, it had 270-odd operational aircraft of all types, tmost of which were single-engine trainers. Not an encouraging basis on which to enter a war. Nevertheless, by the end of five tortuous years, from this tiny cadre of dedicated men the nation achieved the distinction of becoming the world's fourth-ranking air power.

Two views of Felixstowe F.3 flying boats. In the top photo a cine cameraman prepares for a flight for the Fisheries Protective Service. The large photo shows F.3 G-CYBT of the Air Board at The Pas, Man., 1921.

National Aviation Museum, Ottawa

A.M. Narraway/PAC PA19509

(Above) A Curtiss HS-2L flying boat G-CADU of Laurentide Air Service.

(Below) Curtiss HS-2Ls of the Ontario Provincial Air Service, c.1925.

A Loening M23 Air Yacht of the Ontario Provincial
Air Service, Sault St. Marie, 1925.

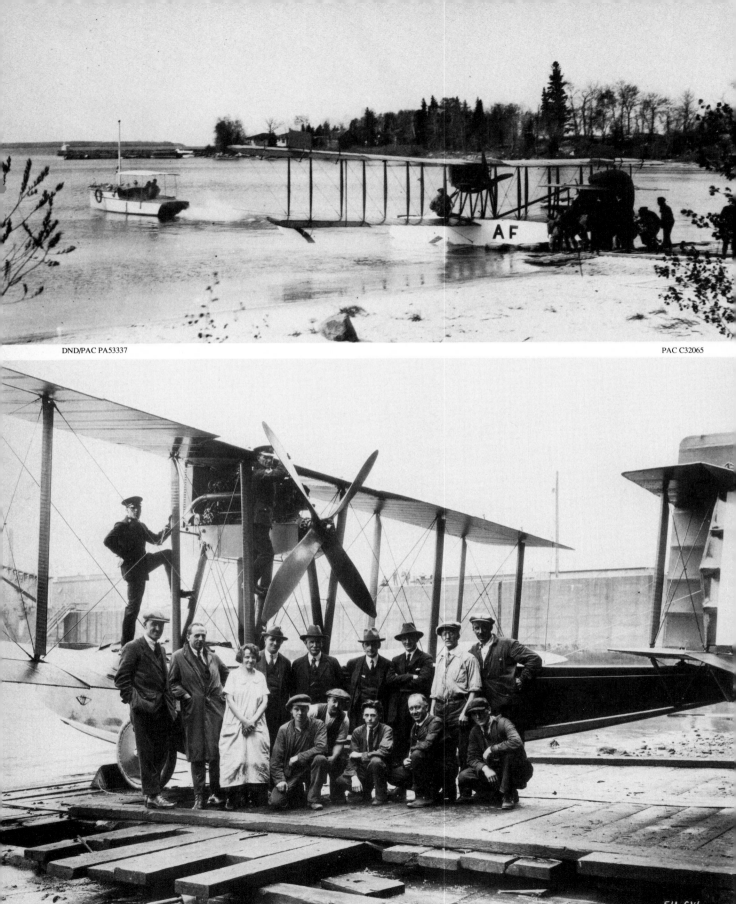

(Facing page, top) Launching Curtiss HS-2L G-CYAF of the RCAF at Victoria Beach, Man., May 28, 1924.

PAC C32613

Three views of the Viking flying boat built for the RCAF by Canadian Vickers of Montreal, July 1923. The photo on the facing page shows workers with the first Viking. The other two show an inside view of the pilots' cockpit and a close-up of the bow hull structure.

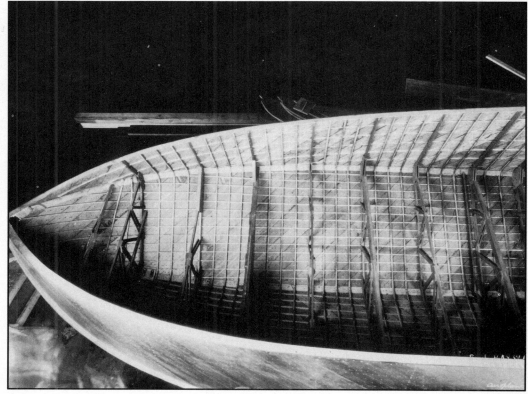

PAC C32621

(Facing page)
Canadian Vickers
Vedette I flying boat
G-CYFS of the RCAF
at Shirley's Bay, Ont.,
September 30, 1925.

(Above) The crew of an RCAF
Vickers Viking IV flying boat,
G-CYET, at Victoria Beach, Man.,
1924. Left to right, Cpl. Alex
Milne, S/L B.D. Hobbs, R.D.
Davidson and F/O J.R. Cairns.
The same aircraft is shown (right)
refuelling at Rabbit River, Man.,

Vickers Vedettes under construction at Canadian
Vickers, Montreal. The first photo shows the hull
ribs and stringers. The second shows final assembly.
This was the company's first indigenous design.

Two views of Avro 552A Viper G-CYGI
of the RCAF at Cormorant Lake, Man.,
1925.

(Overleaf) Canadian Vickers Varuna I of
the RCAF, 1926.
PAC PA20099

De Havilland D.H.60 Moth G-CAHK, grandly christened *Spirit of the Valley of the Moon*, was the first Moth in Canada. It was bought by the Department of Marine Fisheries as a reconnaissance plane for the Hudson Strait Expedition of 1927. The aircraft carried out a number of survey flights but was wrecked at its mooring in a storm after the uncooperative captain of the ice breaker insisted it be removed from the ship. S/L T.A. Lawrence, who flew the plane on the expedition, stands on the float in this photo taken at Wakeham Bay, Que.

(Facing page) Douglas MO-2BS flown by J. Dalzell McKee and S/L A.E. Godfrey on the first trans-Canada seaplane flight, photographed by Punch Dickins near Shellbrook, Sask., on September 18, 1926. The second photo shows the plane on an air mail flight to Saint John, N.B., in 1929. It had been bought by the RCAF after McKee died in a crash in 1927.

Charles Lindbergh taxiing his Ryan NYP *Spirit of St. Louis* at Uplands Airport, Ottawa, a few months after his historic flight to Paris, 1927.

Vickers Vedette Mk.2, 1927. Note the wire mesh between the struts aft of the cockpit to prevent foreign objects flying back into the propeller.

Keystone Puffer at Dartmouth, June 1927, on a delivery flight from Bristol, Penn., to Whycocomagh, N.S., to be used by the RCAF on the first aerial spruce budworm spraying experiments in Canada.

PAC C27057

National Aviation Museum, Ottawa

Fairchilds of the RCAF and Canadian Airways Ltd. on the ice at Lac du Bonnet, Man., c.1928. The nearest aircraft, 'XW, is an FC2, used by the RCAF for photography and as a utility plane until shortly before World War II.

The one and only Vickers Velos. "A beast to fly straight and level" was how one pilot described this 1927 Canadian aerodynamic freak. It had excellent forward visibility for aerial surveying but little else going for it and sank at its mooring at Montreal in 1928.

A Vickers Viking and two Vedettes
at Pelican Narrows, Sask.

PAC PA102338

One of Canada's most famous bushplanes, Fokker Super Universal G-CASK of Canadian Airways was used on the 1930 expedition that flew over the north magnetic pole and discovered remnants of the Franklin Expedition in King William Land. Pilot Walter Gilbert was awarded the McKee Trophy in 1933.

De Havilland Hawk Moth G-CYVM of the RCAF on a dolly at Rockcliffe, Ottawa, October 23, 1930. Three of these aircraft were on strength between 1929 and 1935.

DND/PAC PA62779

52

Curtiss-Reid Rambler with Gipsy upright motor, 1931. The RCAF used a small number of these trainers for primary flying training at Camp Borden. The Curtiss-Reid company was started by W.T. Reid, formerly designer at Canadian Vickers.

(Overleaf) RCAF Vedettes G-CYWK and G-CYWJ at Sled Lake, Sask., c.1930.

De Havilland Gipsy Moths near Camp Borden. The RCAF had 91 of these popular little trainers on strength between 1929 and 1948.

PAC PA120747

RCAF Vedettes G-CYWK and G-CYWJ
at Sled Lake, Sask., c.1930.
RCAF/DND/PAC PA139001

One of the major aviation events of 1931 was the Trans-Canada Air Pageant. To promote aviation, civil and RCAF aircraft travelled across the country, giving 26 flying displays. Shown at right is the Saro Cloud amphibian of W.R.G. Holt. Holt was a son of fabulously wealthy Montreal industrialist Sir Herbert Holt and later financed the development of the Noorduyn Norseman.

(Below) Canadian Vickers Varuna G-CYGV of the RCAF, October 2, 1931. Designed to transport personnel and equipment to fight forest fires, the twin-engine Varuna was based on the hull of the Vedette. It was a sluggish performer.

(Bottom) RCAF Fairchilds at Fort Fitzgerald, Alta., 1931. Nearest the camera is a Fairchild 71B, designed for the RCAF to use in aerial photography.

DND/PAC PA62829

PAC PA14403

De Havilland D.H.61 Giant Moth G-CAPG of the
Ontario Provincial Air Service, Sault Ste. Marie,
May 1933.

A.5.3
REAR LEWIS GUNS
READY FOR ACTION
PHOTO TAKEN DURING FLIGHT
F.8.5- 31/1/36.

Designed for forestry work, the Vancouver first flew in
1929. Later, the RCAF's Vancouvers were armed with
Lewis guns and served on coastal patrol with No.4
Squadron at Jericho Beach, B.C., until replaced by
Stranraers in 1939. The photos on the facing page show,
at top, a Vancouver at the Canadian Vickers plant in
Montreal, and, below, a Vancouver Mk.2. The photo
above shows the rear gun position as seen from the
cockpit of a No.4 Squadron Vancouver Mk.2 in 1936.
Cold work!

Snaps from training days, 1931. Above
is an Avro 504 used at Camp Borden for
rigging instruction, and below is the
Borden "boneyard."

udent pilots at Trenton, 1938. Left to right: Jean rchambault; "Knobby" Fee, who was to make a me for himself in Europe as the "Train Buster" ring the war; Len Birchall from St. Catharines, ho became the "Saviour of Ceylon" (now Sri nka); and Rolf Doucette, who was killed during ining. Birchall, while flying a Catalina patrol the Indian Ocean, spotted the Japanese navy ading for Ceylon and managed to radio a warning Allied forces before being shot down. He was terned for the rest of the war and ended his career an air commodore.

A Royal Navy Fairey Swordfish on loan to the RCAF at Trenton in 1937.

The only recorded case of anyone smiling on the end of a wobble pump. Rod Milne wobbling fuel into a Fairchild 71 at Trout Mills, Ont., 1936.

F/Os Morris and Wylie "checking the manual" on their Vickers Vedette at Sioux Lookout, Ont., 1936.

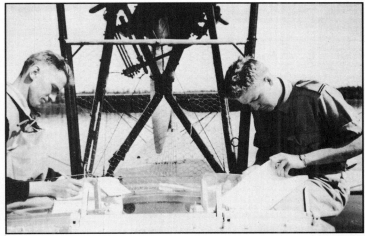

(Facing page) Launching a Stranraer at Eastern Passage Base, 1939, and a Stran in flight over Nova Scotia.

RCAF Norsemans at Oba Lake, Ont., 1938.

All: J. Milne

G.R. Beck Collection/PAC PA123061

Empire flying boat *Cambria* lost a float in a botched landing off Toronto during the Canadian National Exhibition in 1937. Here crew members are seen out on the wing trying to keep the big boat level. Repairs were carried out in a lagoon at Toronto Island.

Refuelling the *Caledonia* of Imperial Airways, Botwood, Newfoundland, July 7, 1937. The nortrhern mail route via Port Washington, U.S., Shediac, N.B., Botwood, Nfld., and Foynes, Ireland, to Southampton began with Pan American's *Dixie Clipper* on June 28, 1939. Two weeks later the PanAm *Yankee Clipper* began a weekly passenger service over the same route with 17 paying passengers on board. Single one-way fare cost $375 (roughly $400 in today's dollars). Britain began its overseas service on August 4 of the same year, flying from Southampton to New York via Foynes, Botwood and Montreal. Harrow tankers based at Botwood and Shannon provided in-flight refuelling. The full program of 16 flights was concluded in September 1939. Both Imperial and PanAm services were suspended the following month because of the war.

G.R. Beck Collection/PAC PA123059

All: John Stroud Collection

(Above) Empire flying boat on the Rochester slipway. (Right) The Martin 130 went into service with Pan American in 1936. (Below) The Short-Mayo composite aircraft was an effort to achieve a longer range. The lower plane, an Empire flying boat, lifted the combination into the air, whereupon they separated and the upper plane, much faster but too heavily loaded to take off unaided, continued on its way carrying mail and newspapers across the ocean. Note the fixed-pitch propellers on *Mercury*.

66

(Facing page) Supermarine Stranraer 910 of the RCAF; and, in the second photo, a Northrop Delta 676 of No.8 Squadron preparing to fly to Sydney, N.S., from Rockcliffe, August 26, 1939. Deltas served on both coasts until 1945. These high-performance machines were almost too hot to handle for novice pilots. One Delta, based on the East Coast, disappeared on a training flight in 1939. Its remains were found in the New Brunswick bush in late 1984.

Blackburn Shark III 525 of No.6 Squadron, RCAF, at Jericho Beach, B.C., May 1939, and (inset) the same aircraft dropping a torpedo.

Lockheed Hudson bomber used for
anti-submarine patrol during 1940-41.

Shearwater Aviation Museum

# WORLD WAR II

Canada declared war on Germany September 10, 1939. Nine days later the first hastily assembled convoy sailed for England. Designated HFX-1, it started what developed into an oceanic "bridge" of ships carrying men, equipment and supplies to the beleaguered British Isles. For HFX-1 the nine Stranraers based at Dartmouth provided anti-submarine patrol over the first 200 miles of the voyage. By establishing aviation fuel dumps on Sable Island, this range of air coverage increased to 400 miles for the second convoy.

Later in the war, convoys were provided with air cover almost continuously from the time they weighed anchor until they arrived at their overseas destinations. Far out at sea, Hudson bombers—later Canso and Catalina flying boats—based in Newfoundland and Iceland took over from the mainland patrol aircraft to provide escort into the middle Atlantic. Sunderland flying boats from Ireland covered the last 500 miles into safe harbour.

The spectacular success of the wartime aircrew training program at Toronto in 1916 had not been forgotten by the British. Canada, they decided, would once again become the aircrew training base for Britain and her allies. Agreement for the British Commonwealth Air Training Plan was signed in Ottawa on December 17, 1939, between Canada, Australia, New Zealand and Britain. U.S. President Roosevelt called Canada the "aerodrome of democracy." Bush pilots, civilian fliers, RAF professionals and U.S. "freelancers" made up the training cadre. By April 1940 the first schools opened. Three years later 97 schools with 184 depots and ancillary units were operating across the country and graduating 3000 students per month. Kingston, Ont., became the Fleet Air Arm training facility.

By war's end, with a training staff of close to 40,000 personnel and using 3600 aircraft, Canada had trained 131,553 aircrew. An incredible achievement. Even more astonishing, 80 per cent of the graduates were Canadians. When war ended the Canadian government generously cancelled Britain's outstanding debt of $425,000,000 ($4.5 billion in current dollars) for its participation in the training program.

Besides operating training schools, the RCAF provided men and aircraft to fight with the RAF overseas while at the same time operating convoy and maritime reconnaissance patrols against German U-boats along the Atlantic seaboard and, later, against Japanese submarines on the Pacific coast. Initially the Stranraers were supported by single-engine Northrop Deltas on floats. Both in turn were replaced later by land-based twin-engine Hudson, Digby and Bolingbroke bombers and long-range Catalina flying boats. The Catalinas—the amphibious versions called Cansos by the RCAF—were capable of 20-hour patrols at a stretch.

To allow land-based aircraft to operate from Dartmouth, runways were built at Eastern Passage Base, a half mile up the hill

Fairchild 71B of the RCAF at Jericho Beach, B.C., 1940. These utility aircraft were also based at Shediac, N.B., and Dartmouth, N.S.

from the seaplane dock, and given the designation RCAF Base Dartmouth. The first six Lockheed Hudsons of No. 11 Bomber and Reconnaissance Squadron arrived from Ottawa's Uplands airport in November 1939. This new anti-submarine Hudson force was led by "Jags" Lewis, an air force regular, who had made a name for himself in the late twenties after being lost on an expedition with Fokker float planes in Hudson Strait. The Stran pilots in the tower watching the Hudsons arrive were given a grand show. One after another the new machines drifted over the runway in a 90-degree crossswind and ground-looped as their pilots attempted three-point landings. Those in the control tower were not impressed.

Three-point landings were abandoned in favour of less impressive but more controllable wheel landings. In the days that followed the rest of the squadron managed to land without incident. As the twin-engine land-based Hudsons, Digbys and Bolingbrokes took over patrol duties the older float-equipped single-engine Deltas retired from Eastern Air Command to the West Coast, where the RCAF also operated Norsemans, Lysanders, Sharks and Goose amphibians.

Naval aviation returned to Darmouth in September 1940 when the Royal Navy established a small base, HMS *Seaborn,* to service RN Swordfish and Walrus aircraft. They used the base also as a recruiting centre to enlist Canadians into the British Fleet Air Arm. The

British Commonwealth Air Training Plan graduated 2629 Fleet Air Arm pilots during the war.

One of them, Robert Hampton Gray, came from Nelson, B.C. On August 9, 1945, in Onagawa Bay, Japan, while flying from HMS *Formidable* in one of the last operational strikes of the war, Gray fishtailed his Corsair wildly through point-blank gunfire from the Japanese destroyer *Amakusa* to release his bomb load and sink the vessel. Moments later his aircraft was seen to flip on to its back and crash into the sea. For his selfless courage Gray was posthumously awarded one of the last Victoria Crosses before hostilities ended. He became the only Canadian fighter pilot and only member of the Royal Canadian Navy to win the award during World War II.

Early in 1941, the first Catalinas and Cansos began arriving from the U.S. Cansos began pouring off Canadian production lines in late 1942. As quickly as crews could be trained the aircraft were put into service. With its uncongested harbour, RCAF Base Patricia Bay on the West Coast became the nation's principal training establishment for the big flying boats. By the middle of 1941, units of Canada's sea wings were also operating on the other side of the Atlantic. During July, 413 Squadron began flying Catalinas on anti-submarine patrols from Stranraer on Scotland's west coast. The next month 415 Squadron formed at Thorney Island as a Coastal Command torpedo-bomber unit

Bellanca Pacemaker transport used at the beginning of World War II.

operating long-range Bristol Beauforts and Blenheim IVs. 420 Squadron based in Northern Ireland used their Catalinas to fly spare Hurricane fighter parts to the Soviet Union, then operated limited patrol activities from various Russian ports while in the area.

Perhaps the most impressive and certainly the biggest anti-submarine patrol aircraft covering the Western Approaches were the Sunderland flying boats. Two Canadian Sunderland squadrons, 422 and 423, based first at Islay in the Scottish Hebrides and later in Northern Ireland at Castle Archdale on Lough Erne, served with Coastal Command from August 1942 until the end of the war.

Despite relatively consistent convoy air cover across the Atlantic in most weather a 500-mile unprotected "gap" still remained along the route. Shipping losses reached a crisis during November 1942 when German U-boats, in an attempt to cut the seaborn supply link from North America, sank the highest tonnage of the war. More long-range and carrier-borne aircraft with better equipment were needed to close the gap. For the next three icy winter months it was touch and go for the Battle of the Atlantic.

By April 1943 the crisis had passed. The gap was closed by the combined use of new improved radar, anti-submarine equipment, small escort carriers, long-range aircraft and MAC ships. The MACs (Merchant Aircraft Carriers) were regular cargo-carrying merchant vessels equipped with either a single

catapult or very short wooden flight deck and capable of carrying one or more single-engine fighters or torpedo bombers. The new equipment produced immediate dividends. During the month of May the Allied navies sank 41 U-boats. The Battle of the Atlantic had been won. When the war ended the RCN's total score for confirmed U-boat kills stood at 28. The RCAF had sunk 27, a fact seldom admitted or discussed in navy wardrooms.

The Royal Navy provided the RCN with the training necessary to man and operate aircraft carriers. HMS *Nabob* and HMS *Puncher,* both Royal Navy carriers, were manned by Canadians under experienced RN officers. As the Canadian efficiency and experience on board the carriers increased, RCN officers in the Executive Branch were encouraged to transfer to the Flying Branch and serve on loan with the Royal Navy Fleet Air Arm. During the war nearly 50 Canadians served aboard RN carriers as pilots and observers.

By the summer of 1944, as the war in the Atlantic wore down, it seemed obvious that the Royal Navy's future concerns would be with the Japanese navy. In anticipation of a prolonged war in the Far East the RN asked for aircrew volunteers from the Dominions. Applications poured in from RCAF pilots, instructors and operational crews itching for action. Those selected were transferred to England in March 1945 to begin their conversion course on naval flying. The number of RCAF aircrews guaranteed the

Canadianization of four RN Fleet Air Arm
squadrons: Nos. 803 and 883 equipped with
Seafire Mk.3 fighters, and Nos. 825 and 826
with Firefly Mk.1 two-seater fighter/reconnais-
sance aircraft. But World War II ended and the
newly trained aircrews were no longer
needed. The Royal Navy returned to its
peacetime establishment.

DND/PAC PA63552

With a roar of engines and clouds of spray, Stranraer 912 of the RCAF takes off at Rockcliffe.

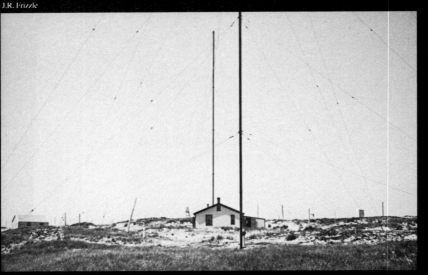

J.R. Frizzle

Marconi radio towers on
Sable Island, 1940.

Shearwater Aviation Museum

Stranraer in flight. Note
the machine-gun mounting
on nose.

Sable Island, showing
Lake Sable where the
Strans landed to refuel
during convoy duty in
1940.

J.R. Frizzle

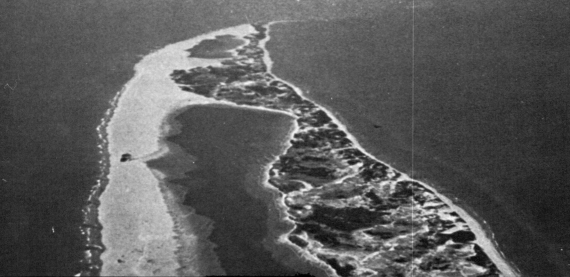

F/L Brock Wiley and
F/L Wilfred Stapleton
"tailing in" their
Stranraer at Lake
Sable, 1940.

The spacious interior
of the Stranraer.

Wiley and Stapleton
arranging Sable Island
pony transport.

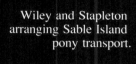

Swordfish landing on MAC *Empire MacAlpine*.

(Below) Left to right, Westland Lysander, Blackburn Shark, Fairchild 71 and Fairey Battle, 1941.

Fairey Swordfish in flight with a torpedo. The "String-bag" had nearly a decade of service with the RN and RCN. First flown in 1934, and powered by a 690 hp Bristol Pegasus, it carried a crew of two or three. Maximum speed was 138 mph at 5000 feet with a normal range of 546 miles. It carried two .303 machine guns and one 1610 lb torpedo or equivalent bomb load. In all 2391 were built. Later versions had a 750 hp Pegasus engine, radar equipment and rockets. No.1 Naval Air Gunners School at Yarmouth, N.S., operated 105 Swordfishes. The Canadian version had an enclosed cockpit to withstand the northern winters. RN crews operating from carriers in the North Atlantic enjoyed no such luxury. The Swordfish had a spectacular career, decimating the Italian navy at Taranto in 1940, helping to win the Battle of Cape Matapan in 1941, and crippling the German pocket battleship *Bismarck* in 1942. Later they were used as convoy escorts and on anti-submarine patrol operating off MAC ships.

Lockheed Hudson Mk.1s of No.120
Bomber Reconnaissance Squadron on
patrol near Patricia Bay, B.C., 1941.

A CAM (Catapult Armed Merchantship)
carrying a Hawker Hurricane at Halifax,
November 1941. A number of Canadian
pilots flew in these RAF operations.

Blackburn Shark II of No.7 Bomber
Reconnaissance Squadron, RCAF,
Prince Rupert, B.C., 1942. Left to
right, F/Sgts Fitzgerald and Miller
and F/O G.A. Doolittle.

(Facing page) Salvaging a Blackburn
Shark III of No.7 Squadron at Prince
Rupert, September 3, 1942, and in
the second photo a Shark II, 504, of
No.6 Bomber Reconnaissance
Squadron, Sea Island, B.C., 1940.

82

Ronny Jaques/NFB/PAC PA115427

(Left) De Havilland D.H.82 Tiger Moths. Over 1500 of these trainers were used by the RCAF in the British Commonwealth Air Training Plan.

(Above) Fairchild Cornells of the "Little Norway" training centre of the Royal Norwegian Air Force in flight near Gravenhurst, Ont., March 1943.

Canadian Forces Photo

Lockheed Vega Ventura GR Mk.5 of RCAF
No.8 Bomber Reconnaissance Squadron at
Patricia Bay, B.C., 1942. Over 200 of these
aircraft operated from both coasts on anti-
submarine patrols and for operational
training at Penfield Ridge, N.B.

Consolidated Catalina IVA of the RCAF
at Rockcliffe, Ont., September 29, 1941.

DND/PAC PA64048

A Sunderland "on the step," and (inset) Sunderlands of Nos.422 and 423 squadrons at Lough Erne, Northern Ireland.

Both: J.R. Frizzle

A Sunderland over St. John's Point, Donegal Bay, Ireland. Evolved as a replacement for the earlier biplane flying boats of the 1930s, the Sunderland, with its 112 ft. 9 in. wingspan, was a military version of the "C" Class Empire flying boats. A gentle, easy machine to fly, it was luxuriously laid out on two decks for a crew of up to 13. It had an officers' wardroom, crew's quarters, sleeping quarters, galley and workshop. The Mk.1 version, with a maximum gross weight of 60,000 lb, entered service in 1938. It was equipped with Pegasus engines giving it a top speed of 140 mph. Later versions used 1200 hp Pratt & Whitneys, which boosted speed to 213 mph at 5000 feet. Normal range was a shade under 3000 miles. Armament consisted of two .50 calibre and eight or twelve .303 machine guns, plus up to 2000 lb of bombs and depth charges. Over 700 were built. Nicknamed the "Flying Porcupine," the Sunderland could give a good account of itself when required. While on patrol over the Bay of Biscay in 1943, a lone Sunderland engaged and shot down eight Junkers 88 bombers. Sunderlands aided in the evacuation of Norway, Greece and Crete. Its single bad habit was shedding propellers. In an engine shutdown the propeller could not be feathered. Invariably the Pegasus engine seized and the windmilling prop then flew clear or through another engine, the wing or the fuselage. Several crews and aircraft were lost in this fashion. The reason was that Coastal Command's low wartime priority resulted in the Sunderland's shaky Pegasus engines being installed without overhaul directly from the overworked Wellingtons of Bomber Command.

J.R. Frizzle

87

Both: National Aviation Museum, Ottawa

Bristol Beaufort Mk.1. Modelled after the Blenheim, the Beaufort torpedo bomber and reconnaissance aircraft remained in operational use with the RAF from 1939 to 1944. 1120 were built. They flew in every theatre of the war. The aircraft had a 1035-mile range with a maximum speed of 265 mph. It carried a four-man crew, four .303 machine guns, and 2000 lb of mines or bombs or one semi-external 1605 lb torpedo. The Beaufort's torpedo-bombing role was taken over in 1943 by the "Torbeau" Bristol Beaufighter.

The Bristol Bolingbroke was the Canadian version of the Mk.1 and Mk.4 Blenheim medium bomber used by the RAF during the early part of the war. When the Blenhein first appeared in 1936, its 266 mph was 40 mph faster than the fighters then in service. It had a range of 1460 miles, carried a three-man crew, 1000 lb of bombs and five .303 machine guns. In all 626 Bolingbrokes were built under licence in Canada and used for coastal patrol duties by the RCAF.

Shearwater Aviation Museum

A Supermarine Walrus catapulted from HMS *Warspite*.
Nicknamed the "Shagbat" or "Pusser's Duck," this single-
engine reconnaissance-spotter and rescue amphibian
designed by R.J. Mitchell was the "eyes of the fleet"
wherever the Royal Navy sailed. The Mk.2 version had a
wood hull with fabric-covered composite wood and metal
wings. Engine was a 775 hp Bristol Pegasus, giving it a
maximum speed of 135 mph and cruise of 95 mph. A few
RN Walruses were kept at Dartmouth during the war as
spares for the RN warships that called at Halifax. After the
war a few served with the new Canadian Naval Aviation
Branch.

6267 LA 10 MAR 44   U/422 R.F. F24 F/S  1600HRS U BOAT ATTACK 50° 52'3"N. 20°19'W.

"Death of a U-boat," 1943. This series of spectacular photos was recorded by the automatic camera on board a Sunderland flown by G/C J.R. Frizzle, during his time as OC of a Sunderland squadron based at Castle Archdale, Northern Ireland. (Above) The U-boat is sighted but before it can dive depth charges are dropped. Explosions follow and the submarine (facing page, top) starts sinking by the stern. The German crew take to their rafts and soon all that remains is floating debris and rafts.

6269 CA. 10MAR 44 //4/422 R.F. F.24 F/5" 1740 HRS. U BOAT SINKING. 200' 5236'N. 2019 W.

6274 CA. 10MAR 44 //4/422 R.F. F.24 F/5" 1740 HRS. U-BOAT SURVIVORS. 200' 5235'N. 2019 W.

Above and below: Shearwater Aviation Museum

(Facing page) Early in the war 14 amphibian versions of the Consolidated PBY Catalina were purchased from the U.S. to provide Eastern Air Command with modern, long-range flying boats. By the end of 1942, Cansos, as the aircraft were dubbed by the RCAF, were being produced in Canada, with 731 rolling off the assembly lines at Boeing and Canadian Vickers. A number of these are still in civil use in Canada.

(Top) Douglas Digby 740 of the RCAF, Moncton, N.B., January 1944. This military derivative of the Douglas DC-2 was used for anti-submarine patrol duties by Eastern Air Command. The second photo shows a Hudson bomber.

J.R. Frizzle

Canso training squadron at Patricia Bay, B.C., 1943.

DND/PAC PA143884

A Fairey Swordfish with torpedo.

A formation of Fairey
Swordfishes of No.1
Naval Air Gunnery
School, RN, Yarmouth,
N.S., 1944.

John Merriman/DND/PAC PA143885

A Swordfish with wings folded on lift ready to
go below to hangar of carrier HMS *Empire
McAndrew,* Halifax, January 20, 1944.

A Seafire undergoing maintenance. This aircraft was the naval version of the famous Spitfire.

A Fairey Firefly Mk.1 hooks on to an
arrester wire as it lands on HMCS
*Magnificent*, February 1950.

# POSTWAR SEA WINGS

The day of the long-range flying boat was over. Future maritime patrol aircraft, it was decided, would be shore-based. The RCAF examined the equipment available in the market and chose the Lockheed P-2 Neptune to replace the lumbering Cansos. This excellent patrol aircraft had a 2200-mile range and maximum speed of 350 mph. It carried an incredible payload of sonobuoys, bombs, torpedoes, depth charges or, when required, long-range internal fuel tanks. As a performance demonstration one Neptune without in-flight refueling flew non-stop from Comox to New Zealand, a distance of nearly 10,000 miles. Powered by two 3500 hp Wright Turbo Compound engines, the compact Neptunes were more powerful and faster than the four-motored wartime Lancaster bombers. More than 1000 were built by Lockheed.  The RCAF's Neptune squadrons were based at Summerside, Prince Edward Island, and Comox, British Columbia.

Although the RN Canadian squadrons were officially demobilized in February 1946, the pilots and RCN personnel who had trained and served with the Royal Navy provided the Canadian navy with the officers and men needed to operate its first carrier. HMCS *Warrior,* one of the RN's light fleet carriers on loan to Canada, was commissioned on January 24, 1946. Two months later she arrived off Halifax with 13 Supermarine Seafire XVs and 9 Fairey Firefly Mk.1s of Nos. 803 and 825 squadrons on board. Off Sambro Light

the *Warrior* swung into wind, its steam jet flowering along the flight deck, and the first squadrons of Canadian naval aircraft took off from a Canadian aircraft carrier for their Dartmouth shore station.

The next two decades were golden years for Canada's naval aviation. HMCS *Magnificent,* a larger British light fleet carrier, replaced the *Warrior* in 1948, and in the same year the Dartmouth base was transferred to the RCN and officially commissioned HMCS Shearwater. Although basic flying training for navy pilots remained with the RCAF, carrier squadron operational training could now be completed at Shearwater instead of sending aircrews to England.

The aircraft were changing too. For reasons of economy and operational compatibility on exercises with the USN, the RCN decided to use American naval aircraft for its carriers . In 1950, the first 25 of a 75-plane order of Grumman Avengers arrived at Shearwater from Quonset Point, Rhode Island, to replace the aging Fireflies. The three-man Avenger had proved its value during the war in the Pacific and in many ways was superior to the Firefly, performing anti-submarine tactics impossible for the Firefly.

One tactic, "Glowworm," involved a hair-raising three-part manoeuvre. It began with a steep dive to increase air speed, followed by a sharp pull-up when several rocket flares were lofted into the sky. With the rockets away, a stomach-raising pushover brought

*Coriolanus*, the last of QEA's Empire flying boats, being beached for the last time after 10 years of service, with more than 2,500,000 miles to her credit.

the Avenger down for an attack on the illuminated sub. So successful were the Avengers that two years later the navy ordered 50 more, bringing the total to 125.

As Avengers replaced the Fireflies on ASW operations, Hawker Sea Furies replaced the Seafires for carrier defence. They were to be the navy's last piston-driven fighter. The Sea Fury, a 460-mph single-seater with a carrying capacity equal to early World War II bombers, was one of the fastest propeller-driven aircraft in the world. With 20mm cannons and rockets its firepower was equivalent to a cruiser's broadside.

In January 1955 the navy finally added jets. Four T-33 Silver Star trainers arrived at Shearwater. A jet conversion training program prepared the navy pilots for the 39 second-hand McDonnell F2H-3 Banshees that were to be delivered later in the year, replacing the Sea Furies. Transition from Royal

Navy to U.S. Navy equipment was nearly complete.

The Avengers, first flown operationally by the USN in the Battle of Midway in June 1942, had also become outdated. A decision was made to replace them with CS2F Trackers. Built under licence from Grumman Aircraft by de Havilland in Toronto, 100 twin-engine Trackers were produced over a four-year period. Deliveries began early in 1956, enabling the Avenger anti-submarine squadrons to be retrained prior to the commissioning of the new 16,000-ton carrier, HMCS *Bonaventure*, then under construction in Belfast, Northern Ireland.

But before HMCS *Magnificent* was paid off, the old carrier served as a transport during the Suez Crisis. She carried 233 vehicles, 4 RCAF Otter aircraft and 100 tons of supplies to the Middle East. On January 19, 1957, in the Mediterannean, the RCAF was given the honour of making the last fixed-wing take-off from the "Maggie's" flight deck as an RCN ship.

HMCS *Bonaventure* became the first Canadian-owned carrier and incorporated features copied from heavy fleet carriers of the

USN, including an angled flight deck. Although both the Trackers and Banshees operated from the "Bonnie," there were misgivings that the ship was too slow, too small and already outdated. Nevertheless, for a time its presence on the Atlantic coast made the Maritimes one of the best defended sectors in Canada. The "Bonnie's" sophisticated aircraft control centre and its Banshees, equipped with Sidewinder guided missiles, provided a highly successful intercept factor in the event of a national emergency. For a long time the Banshees were the only air-to-air missile squadron in the Canadian arsenal.

At the end of World War II thousands of well trained pilots, mechanics and aviation personnel went looking for jobs. It was 1918 all over again—except that in 1945 the numbers were larger. But if the numbers were larger so were the opportunities. Surplus aircraft were snapped up for a song by bush and charter operators across the country. With the post-war boom in mineral exploration, ex-RCAF Cansos, Norsemans and Ansons began crisscrossing the north carrying prospectors, drilling equipment, supplies and passengers, and conducting photographic and electromagnetic surveys. And as in the previous between-the-wars period, aircraft

developed primarily for peacetime purposes found their way into the armed forces.

Fed by a billion-dollar construction program for the DEW, Pinetree and Mid-Canada radar defence lines, bush pilots and operators entered a golden age of profitability and expansion. To meet this explosion of frontier development de Havilland of Canada produced the Beaver in the late forties, following it with the larger single-engine Otter in 1951, perhaps two of the most successful bush aircraft ever designed. Capable of operating on wheels, skis and floats, these ruggedly efficient machines were used for passengers, flying ambulances, cargo, crop dusting, forestry spraying, troop transport, and search and rescue missions by 70 countries around the world. Though more than 1000 Beavers were bought by the U.S. military for use in Korea, where they served as the "Jeep of the air," the Beaver was never purchased by the RCAF. Sixty-nine Otters served with the RCAF between 1953 and 1982. After these suc-

Grumman Goose. The war with Japan brought Canada closer to the war zone. The RCAF operated Goose patrol aircraft along the Pacific Coast, and some remained on strength until 1956.

Shearwater Aviation Museum

cesses de Havilland turned to larger military transport aircraft, the Caribou and Buffalo. The latter, though it cannot operate on floats, succeeded the Grumman Albatross amphibian for search and rescue work in 1969-70. The Buffalo's stable low-speed flying qualities enabled it to drop a dinghy and other supplies with pinpoint accuracy to sailors in trouble.

During the fifties three-seat Bell G2 helicopters with rubber floats or wintertime skids became the acknowledged "gnats" of northern bush operations. They were used to build hydro towers and string lines across the Rockies to Kitimat; they carried prospectors into northern Quebec and helped build the Mid-Canada line. Yet, by a sad twist of fate their whirling rotors sounded the death knell to Canada's naval carrier force.

An Avro Lancaster of Search and Rescue; and (right) a Lancaster crew pose beneath one of its Merlin engines

Both: Shearwater Aviation Museum

Supermarine Walrus II flown
by Sub-Lieutenant A.R. Bray
of No.743 Squadron, RCN,
Dartmouth, N.S., 1946.

Avro Lancaster Mk.10 from
No.404 "Buffalo" Squadron,
Greenwood, N.S., 1946. The
Lanc operated briefly on
maritime patrol after the end
of the war until replaced by
the Lockheed P-2 Neptune.

R.W. Clarke

RCN

(Below) HMCS *Warrior*
at sea.
Shearwater Aviation Museum

"Heaven on deck starts by connecting with number 3 wire. . . " A Seafire lands on HMCS *Warrior* in the Caribbean, 1948.

RCN

(Above) Fairey Firefly taking off from HMCS *Warrior*, 1948. Armed with four 20mm cannon, two 1000 lb bombs or rockets, the two-place Firefly had a range of 1070 miles with a maximum speed of 316 mph. Power plant was either a 1730 hp or 1990 hp Rolls-Royce Griffon XII. Later Firefly Mk.4 versions had clipped wings, the bearded radiator exchanged for extended leading-edge wing type and four-bladed props. The bigger 2250 hp Rolls-Royce Griffon 74 boosted its speed to 386 mph. In June 1948, No.825 Squadron on board HMCS *Magnificent* was equipped with new Mk.4s. The old Mk.1 Fireflies were turned over to newly formed No.826 Squadron at Shearwater. (Below) HMCS *Warrior's* Seafires and Fireflies in the Caribbean.

Both: RCN

(Above) Rolling forward after "disconnect." HMCS *Warrior* in the Caribbean, 1948. (Below) A Seafire prang on *Warrior,* October 1948. At the start of the war the Royal Navy had no first-line fighters of its own. Standard Spitfires with arrester hooks were adopted after trials aboard HMS *Ilustrious* late in 1941. The new design was called the Sea-Spitfire—then Seafire. Over the next four years a variety of improvements and versions appeared: all-metal stressed-skin construction, folding wings and heavier armament. The RCN's Mk.15 Seafires were equipped with 1850 hp Rolls-Royce Griffon VI engines and armed with two 20mm cannon and four .303 machine guns. They had a 430-mile range and a maximum speed of 383 mph.

Both: RCN

Shearwater Aviation Museum

Gollmer/DND/PAC PA141264

(Above) Armorers at work on Fairey Fireflies.

(Right) A Firefly being lowered by lift to the hangar below decks, Halifax, England, March 1946.

(Facing page, top) A Firefly mishap aboard *Warrior*, February 20, 1947. The pilot was Lieut. S.E. Soward.

George Gadde/DND/PAC PA141234

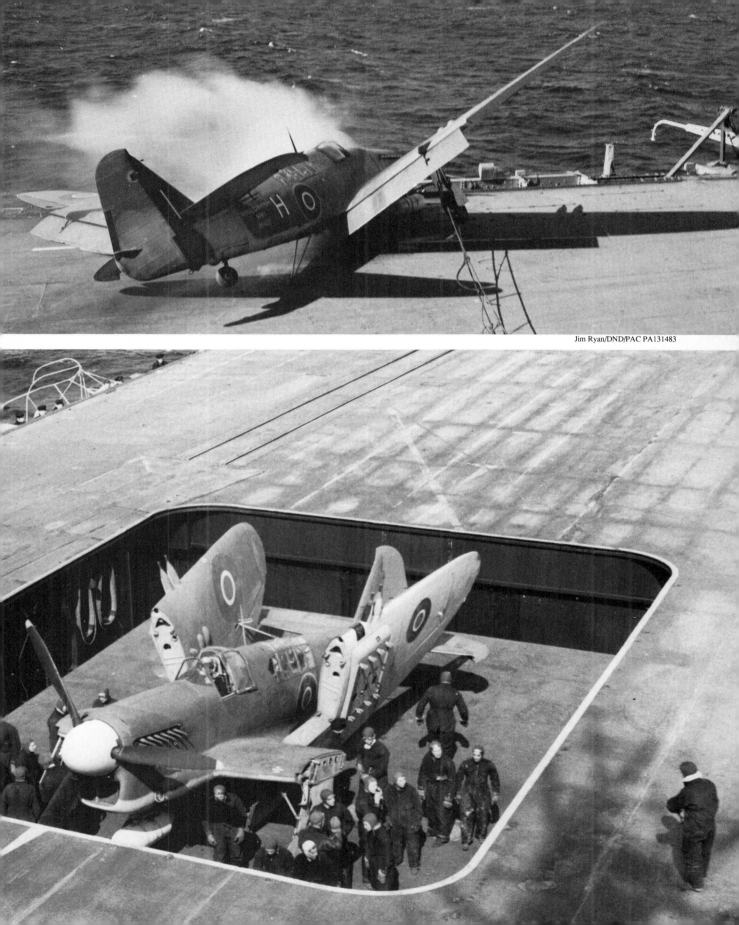

Jim Ryan/DND/PAC PA131483

View looking aft on flight deck of HMCS
*Magnificent,* Belfast, May 25, 1948. On deck
are Hawker Sea Fury and de Havilland Sea
Hornet aircraft.
John Colbert/DND/PAC PA116647

Shearwater Aviation Museum

(Facing page) Two views of Harvards. The North American Harvard advanced trainer used a Pratt & Whitney Wasp radial engine, giving it a top speed of 205 mph. From 1935 to 1945 over 16,000 were built in the U.S., and almost 2000 were built in Canada by Noorduyn in Montreal. The RCN used Harvards in 1947 to qualify students for Seafires. Two Harvards flew from Shearwater to Patricia Bay in 1952 to provide flying training for University Naval Training Division cadets.

RCN Tiger Moth over Dartmouth. This was the standard RAF elementary trainer from 1932 to 1947. Powered by a 130 hp Gipsy Major engine, it had a 93 mph cruise and 109 mph maximum speed. Between 1938 and mid-1942 more than 1500 of these aircraft were produced by de Havilland Aircraft in Toronto for the RCAF's elementary flying schools. The 743 Fleet Requirements Unit of the RCN at Dartmouth Air Station operated a few Tiger Moths in 1949 to give flight experience to non-aircrew members of the service.

Lockheed P-2 Neptune over Vancouver in mid-sixties colour scheme. The power plants of this reliable maritime patrol aircraft were two Wright radial piston engines, plus two Westinghouse J-34 jets. (Inset) Crew member checking the scope.

Both: Shearwater Aviation Museum

(Facing page) Fairey Firefly warming up before catapult take-off from HMCS *Magnificent,* May 1950. The second photo shows hoists being attached to a Firefly that skidded off the flight deck.

An RCN Firefly in a torque stall alongside *Magnificent,* March 1949. This pilot forgot to adjust his rudder trim after a "wave-off" on approach. The surge in power (torque) pulled the nose left. The pilot couldn't hold rudder to keep the nose straight and the aircraft twisted to the left, stalled and went into the sea.

Grumman Avenger over Peggy's Cove, N.S. The RCN operated 125 of these sturdy anti-submarine patrol aircraft. Many still fly as water bombers and aerial spray aircraft.

Variant of the Avenger with a redesigned "camel back" glasshouse canopy aft of the pilot. Note the elongated radar scanner aft of the glasshouse.

Both: Shearwater Aviation Museum

Both: Shearwater Aviation Museum

Avenger with ventral radome. In 1955 four of these aircraft were fitted with large radomes below the bomb bay. The powerful detection gear installed on these "Guppies," as the machines were called, acted the same as shore-based radar installations but with the advantage of airborne mobility. Their job was to search out enemy beyond detection range of RCN ships, then supply information and direct strikes.

(Below) AB Hindross holds chocks at wheels of a
Fairey Firefly aboard *Magnificent,* August 1950.
In the second photo a Sea Fury of No.871 Squadron
takes off toward Mount Vesuvius, September 1951.

A formation of Sea Furies of No.871 Squadron
over Halifax, May 1952.

Sea Fury TG129 of No.803
Squadron, RCN, landing on
*Magnificent,* June 21, 1950.

Both: Shearwater Aviation Museum

A Sea Fury prang ashore—VR919 after a belly landing.

Sea Furies with wings folded for stowing.

Both: Shearwater Aviation Museum

Summer whites aboard HMCS *Magnificent*.

An Expeditor nose-down after a winter landing mishap. The Beach Expeditor was a utility aircraft used by the RCAF and RCN for training and VIP transport.

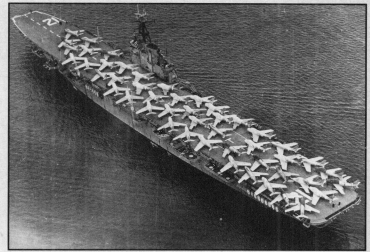

HMCS *Magnificent* returning RCAF Sabres from France and Germany.

(Below) Avenger squadron on board the "Maggie."

Both: Shearwater Aviation Museum

Grumman CS2F Tracker. Note the retractable radome below the fuselage and the magnetic anomaly detector on its retractable boom at the tail. The RCN's all-weather Trackers were built under licence by de Havilland in Toronto. Each cost $700,000 in 1956 Canadian dollars. With a maximum speed of 280 mph and 1350 miles range, the Trackers and their four-man crews became the navy's first twin-engine carrier-based "single-packet" strike and search aircraft. The highly versatile machine fulfilled a variety of roles at sea: anti-submarine search and attack, airborne early warning, deck-landing training, target towing, instrument-flying training, and carrier off-shore delivery of up to 3 tons of cargo or 9 passengers.

The Lockheed T-33 was the navy's first operational jet and was used as an intermediate trainer to convert RCN pilots from propeller-driven to jet aircraft. Although the navy's fighter aircraft have long since departed, T-birds soldier on at Comox and Shearwater, where they tow targets for naval gunnery practice or act as radar targets to enable ships' anti-aircraft teams to practice search and tracking procedures.

Shearwater Aviation Museum

McDonnell F2H Banshee over the clouds. This carrier-based long-range all-weather fighter weighed 27,000 lb fully loaded but could climb at 7000 feet per minute. It had a service ceiling of 43,000 ft and flew at 600 mph. Powerplants were a pair of Westinghouse J34-WE-34 engines of 3250 lb thrust each. Navy pilots trained each year with the army at the Canadian Joint Air Training Centres at Rivers, Man., and Camp Gagetown, N.B. The Banshee served with the RCN from 1955 to 1962.

De Havilland DHC-3 Otter of No.103 Search and Rescue Squadron, Greenwood, N.S., 1959.

R.W. Clarke

HMCS *Bonaventure* at sea with
Trackers and a Sikorsky "Horse"
on deck.

# THE LAST OF THE CARRIERS

It began in 1951 when the RCN's No. 1 helicopter flight was formed at Shearwater with three Bell HTL-4s. These two-place machines with their bubble canopies and dual controls gave the navy the necessary training experience for rotary wing operations. Once their value and usefulness had been proved, the concept of naval helicopters was wholeheartedly embraced by the Department of National Defence.

Early in 1952 the first 12-place single-engine piston-driven Sikorsky HO4S arrived at Shearwater. It went to work for the summer fighting Maritime forest fires, a task the Sikorsky "Horse" continued each year until its retirement in 1969. The establishment of helicopters as a permanent part of naval operations introduced men of the navy's Seaman Branch to aircrew duties for the first time. Airborne sonar dunking, water rescues, cargo hoists, equipment transfers and medical emergencies—all became part of a helicopter seaman's duties.

The first RCN helicopter rescue at sea took place off Newfoundland on a cold October day in 1953 during NATO exercise "Mariner" when Lt. David H. Tate signalled HMCS *Magnificent* that his Sea Fury was losing power. He ditched during his approach a half mile short of the flight deck. The airborne Sikorsky on "plane guard" reached him in 32 seconds and lowered its rescue cable. Moments later a cold and dripping Tate was back on board the "Maggie" warming himself in the wardroom.

Three Piasecki HUP-3 light cargo and medical evacuation helicopters were purchased from the U.S. Army in 1954 to serve on the RCN's new arctic patrol vessel, HMCS *Labrador*. During the summer voyage to the Arctic the following year an Electronic Position Indicator Station was built on Baffin Island. *Labrador* was unable to approach the site closer than eight miles due to shoals and violent tidal streams. Using cargo nets, one Piasecki and two Bells moved 15 tons of building sections, barrels of diesel and lubricating oil, generators, transmitting antennae and provisions ashore in three days. After the *Labrador* was paid off in 1957, all three Piaseckis formed the first and only helicopter component of VU33, the RCN's single West Coast squadron, based at Patricia Bay.

Sikorsky Sea Kings took over from the "Horses" beginning in August 1963. The first four machines arrived from Sikorsky in Stratford, Connecticut. The rest were assembled by United Aircraft of Canada in Longueuil, Quebec. The first of these arrived at Shearwater during September 1964. The Sea King was a vast improvement over its predecessor. Equipped with two General Electric turboshaft jet engines and capable of a 19,000 lb. payload, it had all-weather capability using sophisticated automatic flight stabilizing equipment. The lower fuselage had been designed as a boat hull. Not that it was intended for water landings, but in the event of an emergency a Sea King could force-land on the ocean and either lift off again or remain upright until rescue came.

Before the arrival of the Sea Kings a political decision had been made to retire the aging Banshees and forgo the purchase of a larger and more powerful aircraft carrier. After having the only long-range fighter with Sidewinder heat-seeking air-to-air missiles—and thus the only aircraft in the Canadian armed forces capable of destroying enemy aircraft at long range—the navy suddenly found itself with no air defence at all for its fleet. The RCN's future had been decided. All anti-submarine warfare surveillance patrols would be done by naval shore-based Trackers and long-range RCAF Argus aircraft of Maritime Command. To provide short-range aviation ASW capability at sea, helicopter hangars and flight decks were designed to fit on the St. Laurent class destroyers. The navy's loss of its carrier and fighter aircraft arm was a bitter blow and caused deep resentment.

This dissatisfaction was compounded in 1968 when the nation's political masters decided on a unification program for all three armed services. The resulting loss of individual unit identity combined with a confusion of operational roles in the newly integrated "Canadian Forces" was too much for many old regulars to accept. Some resigned in outrage. Others decided listlessly to wait out their years until retirement and pension. It was a sad period for Canada's navy.

HMCS *Bonaventure* retired the following year and the RCN—now Canadian Forces Maritime Command—became committed to a small ship navy using ASW helicopters tied to destroyer escorts for its sea wings. Without fighter aircraft Canadian naval aviation could never provide more than a supporting role in the event of an armed conflict.

The 28 long-range Canadair Argus aircraft which had replaced the RCAF's Neptunes during the fifties were themselves replaced by Lockheed Auroras in 1982. Operating out of CFB Greenwood, Nova Scotia, the Auroras were the last modern aircraft to join Canada's shrinking maritime aviation force.

In the nearly 20 years since unification, naval aviation has remained virtually static. A detachment of 30-year-old Trackers and even older jet trainers operates on the Pacific coast from Canadian Forces Base Comox on Vancouver Island in utility and fleet support roles. On the East Coast, a squadron of Trackers based at CFB Summerside, P.E.I., is used for inshore surveillance. Two squadrons of aging Sea Kings are based at CFB Shearwater for destroyer escort duties. A third composite squadron with an assortment of T-33s, Trackers and helicopters is used for training and utility duties. Going. . . going. . . gone. . . . Only the pride and memories of those who served remain.

A Sikorsky H04S "Horse" using its hoist to drop supplies.

A Sikorsky "Horse" dunking sonar gear.

Bell landing on HMCS *Labrador*.

A float-equipped Bell.

A Piasecki HUP-3.

An RCAF Vertol H-21, 1960.

Three handsome shots of the distinctive Tracker. These 30-year-old veterans will likely remain in service for years to come. On the facing page a Tracker of VS-880 lands on HMCS *Bonaventure,* and in the second photo a Tracker is seen with its wings folded. Above is a nice formation shot.

Two views of the Grumman Albatross. The photo above shows an Albatross of No.103 Search and Rescue Squadron, Greenwood, N.S., 1965. Ten of these aircraft were ordered in 1959 for use on search and rescue operations. "Albert" was found impractical to operate in heavy seas and was replaced by Buffalos and helicopters.

"Looking like a dragon-
fly in a cocoon" was
how the December 1967
edition of *Crowsnest*
described this Sea King
carried on board in the
hangar of the destroyer
HMCS *Annapolis*. It
is brought down by the
Beartrap, which can haul
the machine down on
to the ship's flight deck
in any kind of weather.

*Bonaventure*
family portrait.
Shearwater Aviation Museum

Shearwater Aviation Museum

Canadair CL-28 Argus Mk.2 on anti-submarine patrol out of Greenwood, N.S., 1965. This sub hunter-killer entered service in 1958. A search radar was installed in a chin-mounted bulge and a MAD (magnetic anomaly detector) sting in the tail. It carried a crew of 15 and 11,600 lb of weaponry. Maximum range was 5600 miles, speed 315 mph. The Argus could remain aloft up to 26 hours, ranging up to 4000 miles from base. After searching 50,000 square miles of sea it could return to base with enough fuel to divert to an alternative airfield 500 miles away.

A Canadian Forces Boeing Vertol CH-113 Labrador. This helicopter, first acquired by the RCAF in 1963, remains the prime search and rescue helicopter today after several upgrades and refits. Labradors have been involved in many notable rescue efforts, including the sinking of the cruise liner *Prinsendam* on the West Coast in 1980.

880 Squadron at Shearwater.

HS-50
Helicopter
Squadron in
a serious
moment,
1968.

Canadian Forces Photo

A de Havilland Buffalo in search and rescue
markings. The Buffalo was acquired by the RCAF
in 1967 as a medium transport aircraft capable of
operating under all weather conditions and from
short, rough strips.

A Sikorsky Sea King in the
West Indies in 1970.

RCN

A Canadian Armed Forces de Havilland Twin Otter. This twin turboprop descendant of the Otter is used in a variety of roles, including search and rescue.

Lockheed Aurora anti-submarine warfare patrol aircraft. Based on the original P-3A Orion design used by the U.S. Navy, the Aurora carries a weapon load of over 20,000 lb, of which over a third may be carried internally. It can remain aloft 18 hours on two engines, 12.9 hours on four. The Aurora replaced the Argus beginning in 1980.